FOR ME, ME, ME

Dorothy Butler knows from experience what
little children enjoy. In this, her first poetry
collection, she has brought us a store of treats.
Here are poems to sing, to jig along with,
listen and sit down and dream about. Poems
indeed FOR ME, ME, ME!

Dorothy Butler runs a children's bookshop in Auckland, New Zealand which includes a reading service, and edits and writes children's books. In 1979, she was awarded the Eleanor Farjeon Award for services to children's literature. *Cushla and her Books* (published by Hodder and Stoughton, 1979) which earned her that award, was based on a study of her severely handicapped grand-daughter. *Babies Need Books*, Dorothy Butler's best selling guide to introducing the very young to books and reading, has been followed by *Five to Eight*.

For me, me, me

Poems for the very young

chosen by
DOROTHY BUTLER

Illustrated by Megan Gressor

KNIGHT BOOKS
Hodder and Stoughton

For Christopher
Hannah
Oliver
Maria
and
Leah
our current pre-schoolers

First published in 1983 by Hodder and Stoughton (Australia) Pty Limited

First published in Great Britain by Knight Books 1988

British Library C.I.P.

For me, me, me : Poems for the very young.
1. Poetry in English – Anthologies.
I. Butler, Dorothy
II. Gressor, Megan
821'.008

ISBN 0 340 49434 4

Printed and bound in Great Britain for Hodder and Stoughton Paperbacks, a division of Hodder and Stoughton Ltd., Mill Road, Dunton Green, Sevenoaks, Kent TN13 2YA.
(Editorial Office: 47 Bedford Square, London WC1B 3DP) by
Cox & Wyman Ltd., Reading

CONTENTS

INTRODUCTION

Poetry and children belong together. Babies are born loving rhythm and the sound of the human voice. Parents instinctively rock and croon to them from birth; surely, the very first song in the world must have been a lullaby!

In the electronic bustle and blur of modern life, however, some of the best things are in danger of being crowded out. For many children, language never becomes that joyful conveyor of fun, wonder and ideas which it rightly is. The trouble is that language is precise and needs to be heard clearly, to be attended to with concentration. The 'near-enough' understanding which children glean from the television screen is a very poor substitute for this sort of understanding. Children deserve better.

I believe that we parents have a tremendous power in our children's lives, and that one of the greatest gifts we can give our children is *language*: as a tool of thought, imagination and self expression. And the easiest way to do this in the very early years is by surrounding them with rhymes, jingles and simple poems.

Why? Because children love to hear language used in this fascinating way, and quickly learn the poems themselves. This helps them to acquire the habit of fluent speech, to build a wide vocabulary, to gain an understanding of the way in which language works to convey ideas, and to enliven everyday life.

The poems in this anthology are those I have used over

many years with my own children, and now with my grandchildren. The collection does not pretend to be 'well-balanced'; it could hardly be so, in the circumstances! Whenever I have encountered a poem which I felt the youngest children in the family might like, I have tried it out and then, if it became popular, copied it out by hand and added it to the old folder in which I keep our favourites. (There is a 'school-age' collection too, which may see the light of publication in due course.)

The only thing that can be said safely is that every single poem in the collection has been tried and tested by the young children in *my* family!

A FEW HINTS ON PRESENTATION:

- Read the poems to yourself first, so that you can be sure of the way the rhythm and rhyme work in each one.
- Try to make each poem a performance. Children love emphasis, expression, gesture and sound effect. In fact, young children are the best audience we will ever have — no need to be self-conscious with this age-group!
- Once you and your children know some of the poems by heart, make a habit of saying them without the book — walking along the road, in the car, anywhere. This gives children the confidence to perform, as well as providing valuable and enjoyable practice in speaking.
- Occasionally, run your fingers under the lines as you repeat the poem. Once the child has learned a particular poem by heart, he or she can then 'read' it aloud, connecting the 'word in the mind' with the 'word on the

page'. This is a great help in learning to read and is easy with poetry, as the rhythm and rhyme support the memory so well.

Above all, make it fun! Parents and children who read together stay in touch. They learn, early in their relationship, to communicate, to share ideas, to talk about feelings. Believe me, this pays off in the years ahead.

Good luck, and good reading!

Dorothy Butler

THE CUPBOARD

I know a little cupboard,
With a teeny tiny key,
And there's a jar of Lollipops
For me, me, me.

It has a little shelf, my dear,
As dark as dark can be,
And there's a dish of Banbury Cakes
For me, me, me.

I have a small fat grandmamma,
With a very slippery knee,
And she's Keeper of the Cupboard,
With the key, key, key.

And when I'm very good, my dear,
As good as good can be,
There's Banbury Cakes, and Lollipops,
For me, me, me.

Walter de la Mare

FUNNY TALK

"Bubble," said the kettle,
"Bubble," said the pot.
"Bubble, bubble, bubble,
We are getting very hot!"

"Shall I take you off the fire?"
"No, you need not trouble.
This is just the way we talk —
Bubble, bubble, bubble!"

Anon

THE LITTLE ELF

I met a little Elf-man once,
Down where the lilies blow.
I asked him why he was so small,
And why he did not grow.

He slightly frowned, and with his eye
He looked me through and through.
"I'm just as big for me," he said,
"As you are big for you!"

John Kendrick Bangs

THE PICKETY FENCE...

The pickety fence
The pickety fence,
Give it a lick it's
The pickety fence
Give it a lick it's
A clickety fence
Give it a lick it's
A lickety fence
Give it a lick
Give it a lick
Give it a lick
With a rickety stick
Pickety
Pickety
Pick.

David McCord

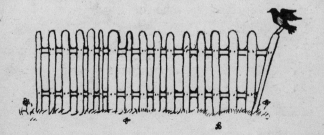

MERRY-GO-ROUND

I climbed up on the merry-go-round,
And it went round and round.
I climbed up on a big brown horse
And it went up and down.
Around and round
And up and down,
Around and round
And up and down,
I sat high up
On a big brown horse
And rode around
On the merry-go-round
I rode around
On the merry-go-round
  Around
    And round
     And
       Round.

Dorothy Baruch

OH, JEMIMA!

Oh, Jemima,
Look at your Uncle Jim!
He's down in the duckpond
Learning how to swim.
First he's on his
Left leg,
Then he's on his
Right —

Now he's on a bar of soap,
Skidding out of
Sight!

Anon

FUZZY WUZZY . . .

Fuzzy wuzzy, creepy crawly
Caterpillar funny,
You will be a butterfly
When the days are sunny.

Winging, flinging, dancing, springing
Butterfly so yellow,
You were once a caterpillar,
Wriggly, wiggly fellow.

Lillian Schulz Vanada

16

CATS

Cats sleep
  Anywhere,
    Any table,
      Any chair,
        Top of piano,
          Window-ledge,
            In the middle,
              On the edge,
                Open drawer,
                  Empty shoe,
                    Anybody's
                      Lap will do,
                        Fitted in a
                          Cardboard box,
                            In the cupboard
                              With your frocks —
                                Anywhere!
                                  They don't care!
                                    Cats sleep
                                      Anywhere.

Eleanor Farjeon

DOWN BY THE RIVER

Down by the river,
Where the green grass grows
Little Polly Perkins washes her clothes.
She sings, she sings, she sings so sweet,
She calls to her playmates in the street.

Patrick, Patrick
Won't you come to tea?
Come next Saturday at half past three;
Tea cakes, pancakes, everything to see —
Oh won't we have a jolly time at half
   past three!

Anon

COUNTING MAGPIES

One for sorrow,
Two for mirth,
Three for a wedding,
Four for a birth,
Five for silver,
Six for gold,
Seven for a secret,
Too precious to be told!

Anon

A LITTLE SEED

A little seed
  For me to sow . . .
A little earth
  To make it grow . . .
A little hole,
  A little pat . . .
A little wish,
  And that is that.
A little sun,
  A little shower,
A little while,
  An then — a flower!

Mabel Watts

19

WISHES

Said the first little chicken
With a queer little squirm,
"I wish I could find
A fat little worm".

Said the second little chicken
With an odd little shrug,
"I wish I could find
A fat little slug".

Said the third little chicken
With a sharp little squeal,
"I wish I could find
Some nice yellow meal".

Said the fourth little chicken
With a small sigh of grief,
"I wish I could find
A little green leaf".

Said the fifth little chicken
With a faint little moan,
"I wish I could find
A small gravel stone".

"Now see here," said their mother
From the green garden patch.
"If you want any breakfast,
Just come here and
                    SCRATCH!"

Anon

21

MISS POLLY

Miss Polly had a dolly
Who was sick, sick, sick,
So she called for the doctor
To come quick, quick, quick.

The doctor came
With his bag and his hat,
and he knocked on the door
With a rat-tat-tat!

He looked at the dolly
And he shook his head,
He said, "Miss Polly,
Put her straight to bed".

He wrote on a paper
For a pill, pill, pill.
"I'll be back in the morning
With my bill, bill, bill."

Anon

FURRY BEAR

If I were a bear,
And a big bear too,
I shouldn't much care
if it froze or snew;
I shouldn't much mind
If it snowed or friz —
I'd be all fur-lined
With a coat like his!

For I'd have fur boots and a brown fur wrap,
And brown fur knickers and a big fur cap.
I'd have a fur muffle-ruff to cover my jaws,
And brown fur mittens on my big brown paws.
With a big brown furry-down up to my head,
I'd sleep all winter in a big fur bed.

    A. A. Milne

THE WOODPECKER

The woodpecker pecked out a little round
    hole,
And made him a home in the telephone pole.

One day when I watched he poked out his
    head,
And he had on a hood and a collar of red.

When the streams of rain pour out of the sky,
And the sparkles of lightning go flashing by,

And the big, big wheels of thunder roll,
He can snuggle back in the telephone pole.

Elizabeth Madox Roberts

THE END

When I was One,
I had just begun.

When I was Two,
I was nearly new.

When I was Three,
I was hardly me.

When I was Four,
I was not much more.

When I was Five,
I was just alive.

But now I am Six, I'm as clever as clever.
So I think I'll be six now for ever and ever.

A. A. Milne

FIRE, FIRE!

"Fire, Fire!"
Said Mrs McGuire.

"Where, where?"
Said Mrs O'Hare.

"Down in the town!"
Said Mrs O'Brown.

"Lord bless us and save us!"
Said old Mrs Davis.

Anon

LAZY HEAD

Get up, get up, you lazy-head,
Get up you lazy sinner.
We need those sheets for tablecloths,
It's nearly time for dinner!

Anon.

MONTAGUE MICHAEL

Montague Michael
You're much too fat,
You wicked old, wily old,
Well-fed cat.

All night you sleep
On a cushion of silk,
And twice a day
I bring you milk.

And once in a while,
When you catch a mouse,
You're the proudest person
In all the house.

But spoilt as you are,
I tell you sir,
This dolly is mine
And you can't have her!

Anon

THE HOUSE OF THE MOUSE

The house of the mouse
is a wee little house,
a green little house in the grass,
which big clumsy folk
may hunt and poke
and still never see as they pass
this sweet little, neat little,
wee little, green little,
cuddle-down hide-away
house in the grass.

Lucy Sprague Mitchell

THE ANIMAL FAIR

I went to the animal fair,
The birds and the beasts were there,
The old baboon by the light of the moon
Was combing his auburn hair.
The monkey, he got drunk,
And sat on the elephant's trunk.
The elephant sneezed and fell on his knees,
But what became of the monk,
   the monk, the monk?

Anon.

DEVOTION

Ginny darling
Lambie pie
Love you
Till
The day
I
Die.

If you ask
The reason
Why
It's because
You are
My
Ginny darling
Lambie pie.

Anon

THE FARMER

A farmer went a-trotting upon his grey mare,
Bumpety, bumpety, bump!
With his daughter behind him so rosy and fair,
Lumpety, lumpety, lump!

A magpie called "Caw" and they all tumbled
  down,
Bumpety, bumpety, bump!
The mare broke her knees and the farmer his
  crown,
Lumpety, lumpety, lump!

The mischievous magpie flew laughing away,
Bumpety, bumpety, bump!
And vowed he would serve them the same the
  next day,
Lumpety, lumpety, lump!

Anon

BABY'S DRINKING SONG

Sip a little
Sup a little
From your little
Cup a little
Sup a little
Sip a little
Put it to your
Lip a little
Tip a little
Tap a little
Not into your
Lap or it'll
Drip a little
Drop a little
On the table
Top a little.

James Kirkup

GOOD MORNING

One day I saw a downy duck
With feathers on his back;
I said "Good morning, downy duck,"
And she said "Quack, quack, quack".

One day I saw a timid mouse
He was so shy and meek;
I said "Good morning timid mouse,"
And he said "Squeak, squeak, squeak".

One day I met a curly dog,
I met him with a bow;
I said "Good morning, curly dog,"
And he said "Bow-wow-wow."

One day I saw a scarlet bird,
He woke me from my sleep;
I said "Good morning, scarlet bird,
And he said "Cheep, cheep cheep".

Muriel Sipe

NO HARM DONE

As I went out
The other day,
My head fell off
And rolled away.

But when I noticed
It was gone,
I picked it up
And put it on.

Anon

BRIAN O'LIN

Brian O'Lin
Had no breeches to wear
So he bought him a sheepskin
To make him a pair.

With the skinny side out
And the woolly side in
"O, 'tis warm on me bottom!"
Said Brian O'Lin.

Anon.

IF I WERE TEENY TINY

If I were teeny tiny
If I were teeny tiny
A mouse could be my pony
And we'd gallop very hard.

If I were teeny tiny
If I were teeny tiny
I would swim when it was rainy
In a puddle in the yard.

I would sleep inside a nutshell
It would make a handsome bed
With a petal for a pillow
To rest my little head.

Oh the things that I would do
Are many many many
If I were teeny tiny
If I were teeny tiny.

Beatrice Schenck de Regniers

LITTLE

I am the sister of him
And he is my brother.
But he is too little for us to
Talk to each other.
So every morning I show him
My doll and my book;
But every morning he still is
Too little to look.

Dorothy Aldis

IMAGINE

Did you ever go fishing on a bright sunny day,
Sit on a fence and have the fence give way?
Slide off the fence and rip your pants,
And see the little fishes do the
    hootchy-kootchy dance?

Anon

TEA-TIME FOR TIMOTHY

Tell little Timothy
   it's nearly time for tea;
The ticker on the mantelpiece
   says half-past-three.
If he wants some tea today
   he'd better come and see.
There are strawberry tarts for Timothy
   and buttered toast for me.

    Clive Sansom

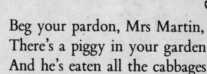

QUICK!

Beg your pardon, Mrs Martin,
There's a piggy in your garden
And he's eaten all the cabbages
And beans.

So you'd better go and thump him
'Cause he's chewing up the pumpkin
And he's trampled on the radishes
And greens!

    Anon

FIVE LITTLE POSSUMS

Five little possums
Sat in a tree
The first one said,
"What do I see?"
The second one said,
"A man with a gun".
The third one said,
"We'd better run".
The fourth one said,
"Let's hide in the shade".
The fifth one said,
"I'm not afraid".

Then BANG went the gun
And how they did run!

Anon

38

ON THE NING NANG NONG

On the Ning Nang Nong
Where the cows go Bong!
And the Monkeys all say Boo!
There's a Nong Nang Ning
Where the trees go Ping!
And the teapots Jibber Jabber Joo
On the Nong Ning Nang
All the mice go Clang!
And you just can't catch 'em when they do!
So it's Ning Nang Nong!
Cows go Bong!
Nong Nang Ning!
Trees go Ping!
Nong Ning Nang!
The mice go Clang!
What a noisy place to belong
Is the Ning Nang Ning Nang Nong!!

Spike Milligan

JEMIMA JANE

Jemima Jane,
Oh, Jemima Jane,
She loved to go out
And slosh in the rain.
She loved to go out
And get herself wet,
And she had a duck
For her favourite pet.

Every day
At half-past four
They'd both run out
The kitchen door;
They'd find a puddle,
And there they'd stay
Until it was time
To go away.

They got quite wet,
But they didn't mind;
And every rainy
Day they'd find
A new way to splash
Or a new way to swim.
And the duck loved Jane,
And Jane loved him.

Marchette Chute

IF I WERE AN APPLE

If I were an apple
And grew on a tree,
I think I'd fall down
On a nice boy like me.

I wouldn't stay there
Giving nobody joy;
I'd fall down at once
And say "Eat me, my boy!"

Anon

SCRATCH, SCRATCH!

I've got a dog as thin as a rail.
He's got fleas all over his tail;
Every time his tail goes flop,
The fleas at the bottom all hop to the top.

Anon

AFTER A BATH

After my bath
I try, try, try
to wipe myself
till I'm dry, dry, dry.

Hands to wipe
and fingers and toes
and two wet legs
and a shiny nose.

Just think how much
less time I'd take
if I were a dog
and could shake, shake, shake.

Aileen Fisher

THE SQUIRREL

Whisky frisky
Hippety hop,
Up he goes
To the tree top!

Whirly twirly
Round and round,
Down he scampers
To the ground!

Furly curly
What a tail!
Tall as a feather,
Broad as a sail.

Where's his supper?
In the shell.
Snappity crackity,
Out it fell!

Anon

CONVERSATION

Chook, chook, chook-chook-chook,
Good morning, Mrs Hen.
How many chickens have you got?
Madam, I've got ten.
Four of them are yellow,
And four of them are brown,
And two of them are speckled red,
The nicest in the town!

Anon

ALAS, ALACK

Ann, Ann!
Come! quick as you can!
There's a fish that *talks*
In the frying-pan.
Out of the fat,
As clear as glass,
He put up his mouth
And moaned "Alas!"
Oh, the most mournful,
"Alas, alack!"
Then turned to his sizzling,
And sank him back.

Walter de la Mare

45

THERE ARE BIG WAVES

There are big waves and little waves
Green waves and blue
Waves you can jump over
Waves you dive through,
Waves that rise up
Like a great water wall,
Waves that swell softly
And don't break at all,
Waves that can whisper,
Waves that can roar,
And tiny waves that run at you
Running on the shore.

Eleanor Farjeon

46

SUSAN BLUE

Oh, Susan Blue,
How do you do?
Please may I go for a walk with you?
Where shall we go?
Oh, I know —
Down in the meadow where the cowslips
   grow!

Kate Greenaway

LILY LEE

I like Lily,
Little Lily Lee,
I Like Lily
And Lily likes me.
Lily likes Lollipops,
Lemonade and lime-drops,
But I like Lily,
Little Lily Lee.

Isobel Best

MY NAME IS...

My name is Sluggery-wuggery,
My name is Worms-for-tea,
My name is Swallow-the-table-leg,
My name is Drink-the-sea.

My name is I-eat-saucepans,
My name is I-like-snails,
My name is Grand-piano-George,
My name is I-ride-whales.

My name is Jump-the-chimney,
My name Bite-my-knee,
My name is Jiggery-pokery,
And Riddle-me-ree, and ME.

Pauline Clarke

PICNIC

Ella, fell a
Maple tree.
Hilda, build a
Fire for me.

Teresa, squeeze a
Lemon, so
Amanda, hand a
Plate to Flo.

Nora, pour a
Cup of tea.
Fancy, Nancy,
What a spree!

Hugh Lofting

IF I HAD A DONKEY

If I had a donkey
And he wouldn't go
Do you think I'd wallop him?
No! No! No!
I'd put him in a stable
And keep him nice and warm,
The best little donkey
That ever was born.
Gee up, Neddy
Gee up, Neddy
The best little donkey
That ever was born.

Joseph Beuler

KINDNESS TO ANIMALS

Riddle cum diddle cum dido
My little dog's name is Fido;
I bought him a wagon
And hitched up a dragon
And off we both went for a ride oh!

Riddle cum diddle cum doodle,
My little cat's name is Toodle;
I curled up her hair,
But she only said, "There!
You have made me look *just* like a poodle!"

Riddle cum diddle cum dinky,
My little pig's name is Winky;
I keep him quite clean
With the washing machine
And I rinse him all off in the sinkie.

Laura E. Richards

I FEEL SICK

Mother, Mother, I feel sick
Send for the doctor, quick, quick, quick!
Doctor, Doctor, must I die?
Yes you must, and so must I!
How many carriages shall I have?
Ten, twenty, thirty, forty, fifty,
   sixty, seventy, eighty, ninety —
   a HUNDRED!

Anon

I'M A NAVVY

I'm a navvy, you're a navvy,
Working on the line.
Five-and-twenty bob a week
And all the overtime.
Roast beef, boiled beef,
Puddings made of eggs,
Up jumps a navvy
With a pair of sausage legs!

Anon

SHADOW DANCE

O Shadow,
Dear Shadow,
Come, Shadow,
And dance!
On the wall
In the firelight
Let both of
Us prance!
I raise my
Arms, thus!
And you raise
Your arms, so!
And dancing
And leaping
And laughing
We go!
From the wall
To the ceiling,
From ceiling
To wall,
Just you and
I, Shadow,
And none else
At all.

Ivy O. Eastwick

MY BANGALOREY MAN

Follow my Bangalorey Man;
Follow my Bangalorey Man;
I'll do all that ever I can
To follow my Bangalorey Man.
   We'll borrow a horse and steal a gig,
   And round the world we'll do a jig,
And I'll do all that ever I can
To follow my Bangalorey Man.

    Anon

THE COW

The friendly cow, all red and white,
I love with all my heart:
She gives me cream with all her might,
To eat with apple tart.

She wanders lowing here and there,
And yet she cannot stray,
All in the pleasant open air,
The pleasant light of day;

And blown by all the winds that pass,
And wet with all the showers,
She walks among the meadow grass
And eats the meadow flowers.

Robert Louis Stevenson

WHETHER

Whether the weather be fine
Or whether the weather be not
Whether the weather be cold
Or whether the weather be hot —
We'll weather the weather
Whatever the weather
Whether we like it or not!

Anon

HAPPINESS

John had
Great big
Waterproof
Boots on;
John had a
Great Big
Waterproof
Hat;
John had a
Great Big
Waterproof
Mackintosh —
And that
(Said John)
Is
That.

A. A. Milne

CATKIN

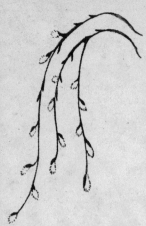

I have a little pussy
And her coat is silver grey;
She lives in a great wide meadow
And she never runs away.
She'll always be a pussy,
She'll never be a cat,
Because — she's a pussy willow!
Now what do you think of that?

Anon

ENCOUNTER

One misty moisty morning,
When cloudy was the weather
I chanced to meet an old man
Clothed all in leather.
He began to compliment,
And I began to grin.
How do you do? And how do you do?
And how do you do again?

Anon

OUR VISIT TO THE ZOO

When we went to the Zoo
We saw a gnu,
    An elk and a whelk
And a wild emu.

We saw a hare
And a bear in his lair,
    And a seal have a meal
On a high-backed chair.

We saw a snake that was
    hardly awake,
And a lion eat meat
They'd forgotten to bake.

We saw a coon and a baby baboon.
The giraffe made us laugh
All afternoon!

We saw a crab
And a long-tailed dab
    And we all went home
In a taxi-cab.

Jessie Pope

WELCOMING SONG

Dance upon silver, dance upon gold,
We have a baby, one day old.

Dance on a peacock, dance on a pearl,
The baby's a sister, because it's a girl.

Dance upon velvet, dance upon silk,
It sleeps in its cradle and dreams about milk.

Dance upon butterflies, dance upon bells,
Its little curled hands are like little curled
    shells.

"Its name?" the wind asks in a whispery
    tongue.
But its name is a secret too dear to be sung.

Margaret Mahy

LITTLE PIPPA

Pip Pip Pippity Pip
Slid on the lino
Slippety Slip
Fell downstairs
Trippety Trip
Tore her knickers
Rippety Rip
Started to cry
Drippety Drip
Poor little Pippa
Pippety Pip.

Spike Milligan

NOT ME!

Policeman, policeman,
Don't catch me!
Catch that boy
Behind the tree.

He stole apples
I stole none!
Put him in the jailhouse,
Just for fun!

Anon

MRS PECK-PIGEON

Mrs Peck-Pigeon
Is picking for bread,
Bob-bob-bob
Goes her little round head
Tame as a pussy-cat
In the street,
Step-step-step
Go her little red feet.
With her little red feet
And her little round head,
Mrs Peck-Pigeon
Goes picking for bread.

Eleanor Farjeon

AWKWARD CHILD

She fell into the bath-tub
She fell into the sink,
She fell into the raspberry jam
And came — out — pink.

Rose Fyleman

THE ANSWERS

"When did the world begin and how?"
I asked a lamb,
  a goat,
    a cow.
"What is it all about and why?"
I asked a hog as he went by
"Where will the whole thing end and when?"
I asked a duck,
  a goose
    a hen:
And I copied all the answers too,
A quack
  a honk
    an oink
      a moo.

Robert Clairmont

THE LITTLE TURTLE

There was a little turtle.
He lived in a box.
He swam in a puddle.
He climbed on the rocks.

He snapped at a mosquito.
He snapped at a flea.
He snapped at a minnow.
And he snapped at me.

He caught the mosquito.
He caught the flea.
He caught the minnow.
But he didn't catch me.

Vachel Lindsay

HA! HA!

Kookaburra sits on the old gum tree,
Merry merry king of the bush is he.
Laugh Kookaburra!
Laugh Kookaburra!
Gay your life must be!

Anon

GOOD MORNING WHEN IT'S MORNING

Good morning when it's morning
Good night when it is night,
Good evening when it's dark out
Good day when it is light,
Good morning to the sunshine
Good evening to the sky,
And when it's time to go away,
Goodbye,
Goodbye,
Goodbye.

Mary Ann Hoberman

WANTED

I'm looking for a house
Said the little brown mouse,
   with
One room for breakfast,
One room for tea,
One room for supper,
And that makes three.

One room to dance in,
When I give a ball,
A kitchen and a bedroom,
Six rooms in all.

Rose Fyleman

THE ELEPHANT

The elephant goes like this and
That,
He's terribly big and terribly
Fat.
He has no fingers he has no
Toes,
But goodness, gracious, what a
NOSE!

Anon

STRANGE

Boots have tongues
But cannot talk;
Chairs have legs
But cannot walk;
Needles have eyes
But cannot see;
This chair has arms —
But it can't hug me!

Anon

JEREMIAH OBADIAH

Jeremiah Obadiah
  puff, puff, puff.
When he gives his messages he
  snuffs, snuffs, snuffs,
When he goes to school by day he
  roars, roars, roars,
When he goes to bed at night he
  snores, snores, snores,
When he goes to Christmas treat he
  eats plum-duff,
Jeremiah Obadiah
  puff, puff, puff.

Anon

MY PUPPY

It's funny
my puppy
knows just how I feel.

When I'm happy
he's yappy
and squirms like an eel.

When I'm grumpy
he's slumpy
and stays at my heel.

It's funny
my puppy
knows such a great deal.

Aileen Fisher

ME AND MY GRANNY

Me and my Granny
And the old grey mare
Kicked up a rumpus
Going to the Fair.

Along came a policeman,
Said "Who's there?"
Just me and my Granny
And the old grey mare!

Anon

TROT, TROT, TROT

Trot, trot, trot!
Go and never stop.
Trot along my little pony,
Where 'tis rough and where 'tis stony.
Go and never stop.
Trot, trot, trot, trot, trot!

Anon

THE KETTLE

There's a little metal kettle
That is sitting near the settle.
You will hear the tittle tattle
Of the lid begin to rattle
When the kettle starts to boil.
What a pretty prittle prattle
Of the kettle near the settle,
Such a merry tittle tattle
When the lid begins to rattle
And the kettle starts to boil.

Gwynneth Thurburn

MICE

I think mice
Are rather nice.

    Their tails are long,
    Their faces small,

        They haven't any
        Chins at all.

            Their ears are pink,
            Their teeth are white,

                They run about
                The house at night.

                    They nibble things
                    They shouldn't touch

                        And no one seems
                        To like them much.

But *I* think mice
Are nice.

Rose Fyleman

71

IT'S RAINING

It's raining,
It's pouring,
The old man
Is snoring —

He bumped his head on the side of the bed
And he couldn't get up in the morning!

Anon

THE GUPPY

Whales have calves,
Cats have kittens,
Bears have cubs,
Bats have bittens.
Swans have cygnets,
Seals have puppies,
But guppies just have little guppies.

Ogden Nash

RUN A LITTLE

Run a little this way,
Run a little that!
Fine new feathers
For a fine new hat.
A fine new hat
For a lady fair —
Run around and turn about
And jump in the air.

Run a little this way,
Run a little that!
White silk ribbon
For a black silk cat.
A black silk cat
For the Lord Mayor's wife —
Run around and turn about
And fly for your life!

James Reeves

MOON-COME-OUT

Moon-Come-Out
And Sun-Go-In,
Here's a soft blanket
To cuddle your chin.

Moon-Go-In
And Sun-Come-Out,
Throw off the blanket
And bustle about.

Eleanor Farjeon

DISASTER

I climbed up the apple tree
And all the apples fell on me;
Make a pudding, make a pie
Did you ever tell a lie?
Yes you did. You know you did.
You broke your mother's teapot lid.
She blew you in, she blew you out
You landed in the sauerkraut.

Anon

CLOUDS

White sheep, white sheep,
On a blue hill,
When the wind stops
You all stand still.
When the wind blows,
You walk away slow,
White sheep, white sheep,
Where do you go?

Christina Rossetti

HEN'S SONG

Chick, chick, come out of your shell.
I've warmed you long, and I've warmed you
   well;
The sun is hot and the sky is blue
Quick, chick, it's time you came through.

Rose Fyleman

MY MOTHER SAID...

My Mother said,
I never should,
Play with the gipsies
In the wood;
If I did, she would say,
"Naughty little girl to disobey.
Your hair won't curl,
And your eyes won't shine,
You gipsy girl,
You shan't be mine!"

And my father said that if I did
He'd rap my head with the teapot lid.
The wood was dark, the grass was green,
In came Sally with a tambourine.
I went to sea — no ship to get across;
I paid ten shillings for a blind white horse;
I up on his back and was off in a crack,
Sally, tell my mother I shall never come back!

Anon

MICHAEL FINNIGIN

There was an old man
Called Michael Finnigin
He grew whiskers on his chinnigin
The wind came up
And blew them in again
Poor old Michael Finnigin,
  begin again!

  Anon

HOW MANY MILES TO BABYLON?

"How many miles is it to Babylon?"
  "Three score miles and ten."
"Can I get there by candlelight?"
  "Yes, and back again!
If your heels are nimble and light,
You may get there by candlelight."

  Anon

SOME ONE

Some one came knocking
At my wee small door;
Some one came knocking,
I'm sure — sure — sure;
I listened, I opened,
I looked to left and right,
But nought there was a-stirring
In the still dark night;
Only the busy beetle
Tap-tapping in the wall,
Only from the forest
The screech-owl's call,
Only the cricket whistling
While the dewdrops fall,
So I know not who came knocking,
At all, at all, at all.

Walter de la Mare

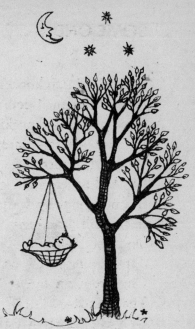

LULLABY

Sleep, baby, sleep,
Thy father guards the sheep.
Thy mother is shaking the dreamland tree
And down falls a little dream on thee.
Sleep, baby, sleep.

Sleep, baby, sleep,
The large stars are the sheep.
The little ones are the lambs, I guess,
The gentle moon is the shepherdess.
Sleep, baby sleep.

Anon

A CHRISTMAS BLESSING

God bless the master of this house,
    The mistress also,
And all the little children
    That round the table go;
And all your kin and kinsmen
    That dwell both far and near;
I wish you a Merry Christmas,
    And a Happy New Year.

    Anon

ACKNOWLEDGEMENTS

For permission to use copyright material we thank the following:

Associated Book Publishers Ltd and Mr C. R. Milne for "The End" and "Furry Bear" from *Now We Are Six*; "Happiness" from *When We Were Very Young* by A. A. Milne.

A. & C. Black Publishers Ltd, London, for "Lily Lee" by Isobel Best and "Tea-time for Timothy" by Clive Sansom.

Marchette Chute for "Jemima Jane".

Curtis Brown Ltd, New York, for "The Guppy" by Ogden Nash, copyright © 1944 by Ogden Nash.

E. P. Dutton Inc., New York, for "Shadow Dance" from *Fairies and Suchlike* by Ivy O. Eastwick, copyright © 1946 by E.P. Dutton & Co. Inc., renewed, 1974, by Ivy O. Eastwick; and "The House of the Mouse" from *Another Here and Now Story Book* by Lucy Sprague Mitchell, copyright, 1937, by E. P. Dutton & Co., Inc., renewed, 1965 by Lucy Sprague Mitchell.

Aileen Fisher for "After a Bath" and "My Puppy", from *Up the Windy Hill*, Abelard, N.Y., 1953, copyright renewed 1981.

Harcourt Brace Jovanovich, Inc., New York, for "If I were Teeny Tiny" from *Something Special* © 1958 by Beatrice Schenck de Regniers.

David Higham Associates Limited for "Cats" and "Moon-come-out" from *Silver-Sand and Snow*, "These are Big Waves" and "Mrs Peck-Pigeon" from *The Garden Wall* by Eleanor Farjeon.

Mary Ann Hoberman for "Good Morning when it's Morning" from *Nuts to You and Nuts to Me* (Albert Knopf).

Bertha Klausner International Literary Agency, Inc., New York, for "Merry-go-round" by Dorothy Baruch from *I Like Machinery* (Harper Bros).

The Literary Trustees of Walter de la Mare and the Society of Authors as their representative for "The Cupboard", "Alas, Alack" and "Someone".

Little, Brown & Co. for "The Pickety Fence" from *Far and Few* by David McCord © 1952 by David McCord, and "Kindness to Animals" from *Tirra Lirra: Rhymes Old and New* by Laura E. Richards © 1932 by Laura E. Richards, © renewed by Hamilton Richards.

Macmillan Publishing Company Inc., N.Y., for "The Little Turtle" by Vachel Lindsay from *Collected Poems*, copyright 1922 by Macmillan Publishing Company Inc., renewed 1948 by Elizabeth C. Lindsay.

Margaret Mahy for "Welcoming Song" from *The First Margaret Mahy Story Book* (Dent).

Spike Milligan for "Little Pippa" and "On the Ning Nang Nong".

Oxford University Press for "Run a Little" from *The Blackbird and the Lilac* by James Reeves (1952).

Pergamon Press Ltd for "Baby's Drinking Song" by James Kirkup.

G.P. Putnam's Sons for "Little" from *Everything and Anything* by Dorothy Aldis, copyright 1925, 26, 27, renewed © 1953, 54, 55 by Dorothy Aldis.

Muriel Sipe and the Association for Childhood Education International for "Good Morning" from *Sung under the Silver Umbrella*.

The Society of Authors as Literary Representatives of the Estate of Rose Fyleman for "Awkward Child" (first verse), "Hen's Song", "Mice", "Wanted".

Lillian S. Vanada and the Association for Childhood Education International for "Fuzzy, Wuzzy, Creepy Crawly".

Viking Penguin Inc., New York, for "The Woodpecker" from *Under the Tree* by Elizabeth Madox Roberts, copyright 1922 by B. W. Huebsch Inc., copyright 1930 by the Viking Press Inc., copyright renewed 1950, 1958 by Ivor S. Roberts.

The publishers have made every effort to trace copyright holders, in some cases without success. We would be grateful to hear from any copyright holders not here acknowledged.

INDEX to AUTHORS, Titles and
first lines

A CATALOGUE OF COMIC VERSE

Collected and illustrated by Rolf Harris

. . . or cattle dog, as they say in Australia, jam-packed with great poems on a variety of different topics – including cats and dogs – to say nothing of tigers and terrified tortoises, some rather curious eating habits and a host of loony relations!

KNIGHT BOOKS

I WILL BUILD YOU A HOUSE

Edited by Dorothy Butler

From Robert Louis Stevenson and Charles Causley to Spike Milligan and Anon. Here is an entire poetry house for the young.

A second marvellous collection of poems for the very young compiled by Dorothy Butler, author of *Babies Need Books* and *Five to Eight*.

KNIGHT BOOKS

A FOOTPRINT ON THE AIR

Selected by Naomi Lewis

In this superb collection of verse by poets like Edward Thomas, Sylvia Plath and Charles Causley, some unique essence of each animal, each bird, each flower, has been captured. It is an anthology which will bring you very close to nature – perhaps for the first time . . .

KNIGHT BOOKS

PUDDINGS AND PIES

Compiled by Iris Grender

Little Jack Horner, The Queen of Hearts and Little Miss Muffett.

Traditional rhymes are frequently concerned with food – as are little children! This collection of rhymes serves up new and less familiar verse to accompany the very best of the old favourites. The result is a feast for young and old alike.

KNIGHT BOOKS